Printed and published by D. C. Thomson & Co Ltd.,
185 Fleet Street, London EC4A 2HS.
ISBN 1 84535 156 8

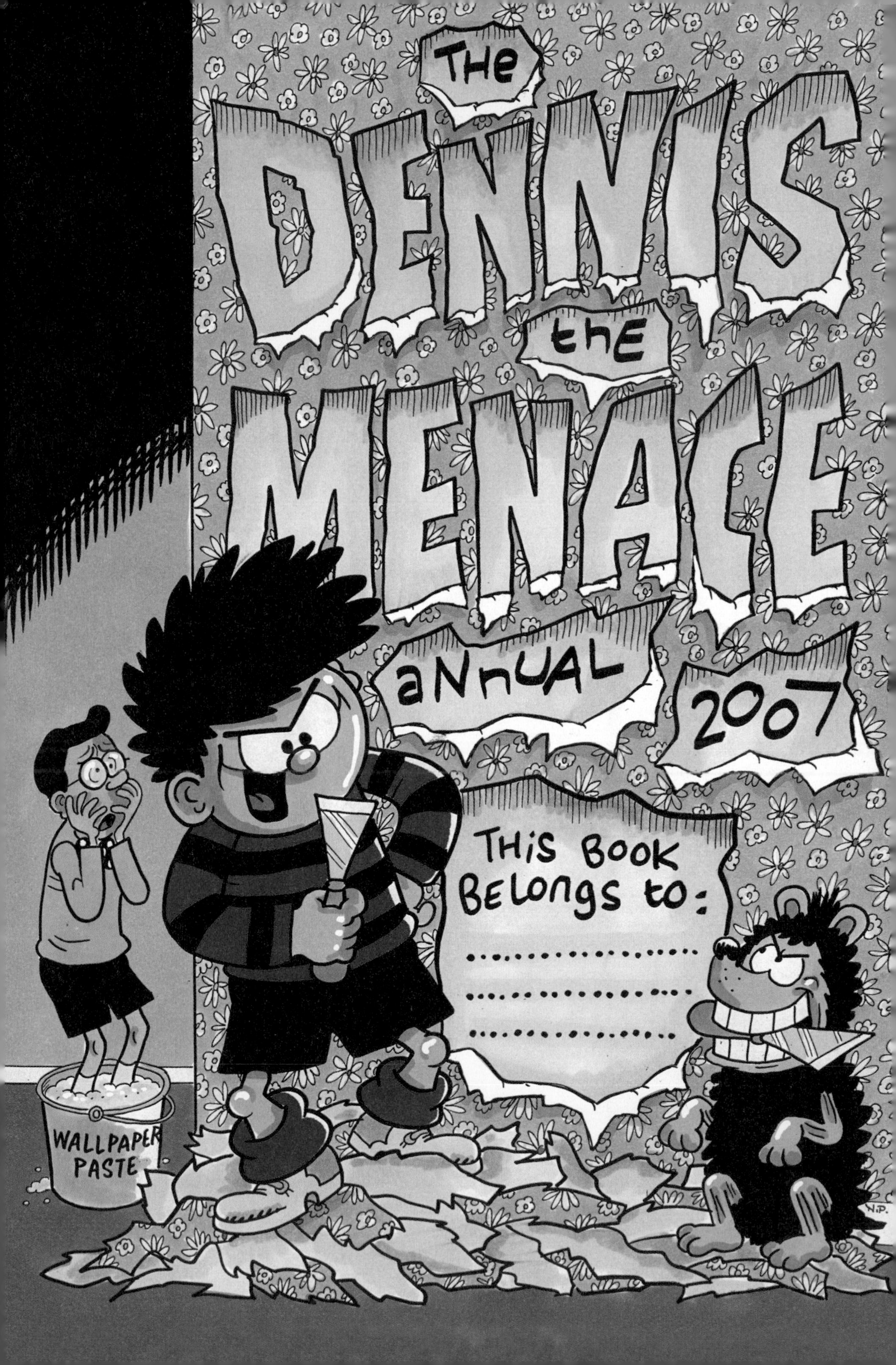
THE
DENNIS
the
MENACE
aNnUAL
2007
THIS BOOK
BELongs to:
WALLPAPER
PASTE

LET SLEEPING MENACES LIE!

CAN'T LET YOU SEE DENNIS SLEEPING LIKE A SOFTY, READERS!
GNASH! GNASH! GNASH!
EH? WHAT'S GOING ON?
Dennis wakens up!
SNARL! WHO HAS PILED ALL THESE SOFTY TOYS ON MY BED WHILE I WAS SLEEPING?
I THINK I CAN GUESS. THERE'S A TRAIL LEADING TO...
GYUK!
...MY LITTLE SISTER'S ROOM!
BEA'S ROOM
BEA IS ALWAYS TRYING TO SWAP HER BABY TOYS FOR MY MENACING GEAR! GIMME THEM BAC
YOU DO REALISE, THIS MEANS...
NO CHANCE, BIG BRUVVER! ME LIKES YOUR FINGS BETTER!
...A BATTLE!
NAH – A BOTTLE!
GNERK!

LOOK OUT, GNASHER! INCOMING MISSILE!
GNULP!
DUCK!
ME FROW SCRUMMY FRISBEES!
BABY NOSH RUSKS
FLING!
GNURPH!
ZING!
SPLAD!
GREAT SHOT, BEA!
HOLD IT, GNASHER.
GNRRR!!
BEA WANTS TO TALK PEACE.
WHISPER. WHISPER.
GOOD IDEA!
AGREED! A TRUCE BETWEEN ALL US MENACES!
SLAP!
YEAH!
SO BEA CAN KEEP SOME OF MY MENACING STUFF, AND WE KEEP SOME OF HER CUDDLY TOYS.
GNEH? WHAT FOR?
Denniz Bea Gnasher
TARGET PRACTICE! WAHEY!
YER! SO WE'S ALL GOOD SHOTS FER NEXT TIME WE SEE ANY SOFTIES!
I SAY! I SIMPLY MUST PROTEST AT THAT AWFULLY VIOLENT LAST PICTURE. AND AT THE IMPLIED THREAT TO WE SOFT CHAPS!

BEA A GOOD GIRL!
HAR-HAR! IT'S A GREAT BIT OF MENACING, TAKING BEA OUT IN HER BUGGY!
PING! TING! PING!
OW!
EEK!
I SAY! AMPHIBIOUS ASSAULT!
MEOWL!!!!
GNEE-HEE!
DIS ISSA LAFF!

THAT BUGGY IS A MENACING MACHINE!
AT LEAST THEY DIDN'T CATAPULT US!
THAT'S WHAT YOU THINK!
WATCH AND LEARN, BEA!
BRAKE!
SCREECH!
THIS BUGGY HAS EVERY WEAPON WE NEED! HA-HA! BULL'S-EYE!
SPLOT!
SPLOT!
SPLOT!
GOTCHAS!
PYOING!
TWANG!
MENACES!
THAT'S US!
GNEVER FORGET IT.
WE'LL CATCH UP WITH YOU SOON ENOUGH!
Shortly –
AHA! WE SPY SOFTIES!
SCREECH!
TRA-LA-LA!
MINCE!
Ballet practice!
PRANCE!
THAT'S IT, GNASHER. FIX THOSE ONTO THE BUGGY WHEELS.
GNIFTY IDEA, DENNIS!
TEE-HEE-HEE! LOOK AT DENNIS AND GNASHER – PUSHING A BABY'S BUGGY!
WOO-HOO-HOO! HOW SOFT! JUST LIKE US!
WELCOME TO SOFTYNESS, MENACES!
TICKLE -ICKLE!
OH, YEAH? HAVE SOME OF THIS!
EEEEEEKKK! HOW AWFUL! A KNEE-TICKLING FEATHER ATTACK! TITTER!
WE SHALL TELL OUR PARENTS! CHUCKLE!
OUR POOR KNOBBLY KNEECAPS! CHORTLE!
UNCONTROLLED MIRTH!
LET'S GO, MENACES.

WAIT A MINUTE, BEA! YOU HAVEN'T DONE ANY MENACING YET!
SCREECH!
GYEAH! YOUR TURN!
EH? WHAT'S UP?
NNNNGHHHH!!!!....
BURBLE!
WOW! WHAT AN ERUPTION!
GNEEK!
GAG! WHEW! GUESS WHAT BEA HAS DROPPED!
HAAA! GOOD 'UN!
GNIPOO!!!!....
MOAN! GRUMBLE!
AND NOT A MOMENT TOO SOON!
SO! WE'VE CAUGHT YOU AT LAST, MENACES! NOW LISTEN HERE, DE... YEUCH!!!!!!....
GROO!
GAG!
WHAT A GREAT MENACE IN THE MAKING! BEA KEPT THAT SECRET WEAPON 'UP HER SLEEVE'! HO-HO!
OOOO! A NOSTRIL-SQUISHING NIFF!
GAS! PANIC!
RETREAT! RAPIDLY! RANCID GAS ATTACK.
GNEE-HEE!

GANGWAY!
GNUMPH!!!!!!

THIS SHOULD BE FAR ENOUGH AWAY.
FAR ENOUGH AWAY!
GNAAARSHOOOOO!
LET IT OUT, PAL!
SNEAK!
TIPTOE!
LET ME EXPLAIN, READERS! WE WERE SNEAKING OUT FOR A SPOT OF MENACING. BUT BEA WAS HAVING HER AFTERNOON NAP.
OH, NO!
CRUNCH!
AND I TROD ON POOR GNASHER'S PAW BY MISTAKE!
GNUMPH!
I HAD TO STOP GNASHER'S YELL AND RUN FOR IT!
YEAH! WE DIDN'T WANT TO WAKEN BEA!
GNO WAY!
TIME FOR SOME MENACING, I'D SAY!
YOU BET!
PREPARE PEA SHOOTERS!
SIMPER!
YIKES!
But –
PUFF!
BLOW!
HOW NICE!
FWHPH!
LOVELY!
FLOWERY NIFF!
POWDERY PONG!
WHAT'S THIS?
A BABY TALCUM POWDER ATTACK!
SMELLS DIVINE!
TA, MENACES!

LET'S SEE HOW THE SOFTIES LIKE A CATAPULT ATTACK!
AMMO
AMMO
TWANG!
TWANG
HUH? WHAT NOW?
COTTON WOOL BALLS! HOW NICE!
FLUMP!
FLOP!
BAH! SOMEONE IS GOING TO PAY FOR PLAYING TRICKS ON US MENACES! THEY'VE SWAPPED OUR USUAL AMMO OF PEAS AND ROTTEN TOMATOES FOR BABY STUFF.
AMMO
'BYE, MENACES! OR SHOULD WE CALL YOU SOFTIES? SMIRK!
GRR! NOW WHO COULD HAVE DONE THIS TO US?
Back home, the menaces see who the tricksters are —
SO! MUM AND DAD SWAPPED OUR AMMO, EH?
GREAT TRICK WE PLAYED ON THE MENACES!
HO-HO! YES!
MUFFLED TICK!
SILENT TITTER!
COTTON WOOL BALLS
WELL, THEY HAVEN'T OUT-MENACED THE MENACES YET! WE'LL FIX THEM.
GNUH? HOW?
LIKE THIS
DRING! DRING! DRING!
OH, NO! THE PHONE!
OH, NO! IT'S WOKEN BEA!
WAAAAA!
WAAA
HELLO?
OOPS! SORRY, DAD! DID I WAKEN MY LITTLE SISTER? HOW SORRY I AM! NOT!
COME ON, GNASHER! WE'LL KEEP WELL AWAY FROM HOME TILL BEA STOPS CRYING! WHAT A DIN MUM AND DAD WILL HAVE TO PUT UP WITH – SERVES THEM RIGHT FOR TRICKING US!
YEAH! WHAT A PAIR OF LUNGS BEA HAS!

KING KONG
WE DON'T HAVE ANY HORROR DVDS OR BOOKS IN OUR HOUSE. DO YOU KNOW WHY, READERS?
IT'S BECAUSE WE HAVE OUR OWN HORRIFIC, HORRIBLE MONSTERS – THE MENACES!
BEANOTOWN BATHS
SQUEAL!!!!! A GREAT BIG HAIRY APE!
SHOWERS
GNEE-HEE! ONL
DENNIS! HE DOESN'T
SHOWER GEL, HE U
BROWN SAUCE!
FRANKENSTEIN
EEEK! THAT FUNNY WALK! MUST BE FRANKENSTEIN'S MONSTER!
BEA'S ONLY WALKING STRANGELY 'COS SHE'S JUST FILLED HER NAPPY!
FULL!
SCARPER!
AGAIN!
LOCH NE
MONSTE
SILLY SOFTIES! I'M NOT THE LOCH NESS MONSTER! I'M JUST HAVING A MUD BATH!
PARP!
WHIMPER!
SQUEAL!

WEREWOLF
HOWL!!
OOOO!!! A HOWLING WEREWOLF! WAAAH!!
YOU'D HOWL LIKE GNASHER, TOO - IF YOU WERE SITTING ON COLD LINO LIKE HIM! FREEZING HIS BOTTY IT IS!
BUT MORE HORRIFYING AND HORRIFIC THAN ALL THAT...
WE'VE HAD ENOUGH OF YOU MENACES BEHAVIOUR. TIME YOU LEARNED TO BE NICE.
THE MUMMY
...WE'VE BEEN SENT TO WALTER'S TEA PARTY! THIS IS MONSTROUS!
GNO!!!
NOW, SHALL I BE MUMMY?

RUDE WORDS YOU CAN GET AWAY WITH!
BUM!
SHRIEK!!!!
BEA! HOW RUDE!
GOOD ONE, BEA! LET ME CHECK IT.
DICTIONARY
BUT IT'S NOT RUDE AT ALL. IT'S AN AMERICAN SLANG WORD FOR A TRAMP! SEE, YOU CAN GET AWAY WITH IT!
HEE-HEE! AN' ME'LL GIVE YA MORE NOT REALLY RUDE WORDS YOU CAN GET AWAY WIV LATER IN DA ANNUAL, READERS!

ALL WASHED UP!
WAHEY! GREAT WATER SLIDE, DAD!
DENNIS!
GNASHEE!!!!
HEE-HEE!

Rasher is feeling left out!
THAT LOOKS OINKINGLY GOOD FUN!
SLIDE!
GRRR!!!! LOOK AT MY CAR! GET A CLOTH AND WIPE OFF THAT MUCK, DENNIS. AT ONCE!
SPLART!
OINKY!
WHERE CAN I FIND A CLOTH, I WONDER?
HELLO, MY PRETTY LITTLE FLOWER! HOW ARE YOU TODAY?
DUST
MIND IF I BORROW THIS OLD RAG OF YOURS, OLD PAL? NO? HOW KIND!
WAAHHH! MY COMFORT BLANKET! RETURN IT IMMEDIATELY! OR I'LL SCREAM UNTIL I'M LIVID!
SO, YOU WANT IT BACK, WATTIE? FAIR ENOUGH.
EEEEEEEEEEEEK! I'LL NEVER BE ABLE TO GO TO SLEEPY-BYES NOW! MY COMFORT BLANKET IS MUCKIER THAN BEA'S PANTS! AFTER A CURRY.
SOB! WAIL! CRY! BOO-HOO! BUBBLE!
WHAT A SOFTY DIN! I'LL HAVE TO DO SOMETHING!
So –
HERE YOU ARE, WALTER! YOU CAN HAVE GNASHER'S BLANKET!
GHMM!
WELL, IF GNASHER DOESN'T MIND.
Soon –
GNOT AT ALL, GNOT IF YOU DON'T MIND MY FLEAS!
ITCH!
SCRATCH!
WRIGGLE!
OO! AA! IT'S FULL OF FLEAS! NASTY FELLERS!

HOW ABOUT BEA'S DOLLY'S BLANKET?
PYOING! PYOING!
PYOING!
'AVE IT! ME NO WANT IT!
DON'T BE SILLY. DOLLY WOULD CATCH A FRIGHTFUL CHILL WITHOUT HER BLANKET.
BIFF!
SWIPE!
TUCK!
DOPEY BRUVVER! HE'S GIMMIED IT BACK!
Just then –
COULD YOU USE THIS AS A COMFORT BLANKET, WALTER?
WHY, YES! THANK YOU, CURLY!
Dennis's pal, Curly Menace.
BUT WHY DOES IT HAVE THE NUMBER 7 ON IT?
'COS I GOT IT FROM THE GOLF COURSE! 7TH HOLE!
THWACK! THWACK!
THWACK!
TONK! BOK!
TOK!
DOINK!
GNA HA!
GOOD SHOOTING, GOLFERS!
WHIMPER!
WAIL! HOWL!
OOO! WALTER'S WAILING AGAIN! WE CAN'T TAKE MUCH MORE OF HIS RACKET.
GET HIM A PIECE OF CLOTH TO QUIETEN HIM – QUICK!
So, quickly –
LOOK WHAT GNASHER HAS FETCHED FOR YOU, WALTER!
OO! HOW KIND OF HIM! I'M SO TOUCHED!
HMMM! IT'S LOVELY! IT EVEN SMELLS OF MY FAVOURITE PERFUME!
IT'S THE NICEST THING GNASHER'S EVER GIVEN ME!
HAW-HAW! LOOK WHERE GNASHER GOT IT FROM!
WATTIE'S BACK SIDE! HA-HA! HE WAS WAILING SO MUCH, HE DIDN'T HEAR GNASHE
RIP IT OFF!

PARTY ON, MENACES!

HAPPY BIRTHDAY PIE-FACE
PIN THE CRUST ON THE PIE
PIES
PIE SANDWICHES
BIRTHDAY PIE
JELLY PIE
COCKTAIL PIES
COOL! A PIE! JUST WHAT I'VE ALWAYS WANTED!
CAREFUL, PIE-FACE! IF YOU EAT TOO MANY PIES, YOU'LL TURN INTO ONE!
RUBBISH, DENNIS! I WON'T...
GOBBLE! SLURP!
...WILL I? GULP!
NO WAY! I WAS ONLY KIDDING!
WHEW! THAT'S A RELIEF.
LET'S HAVE SOME FUN WITH THIS PIE DISH.
At Beanotown pond—
IT MAKES A GREAT BOAT.
WE'LL NEED SOME OARS.
YOU COULD USE SOME OF OLIVE'S COOKERY TROPHIES, LADS.
OLIVE? THE BASH STREET COOK?
OLIVE? THE USELESS BASH STREET COOK?
SURELY OLIVE HAS NEVER WON ANY TROPHIES FOR HER TERRIBLE COOKING!

THEY'RE NOT REALLY TROPHIES – THEY'RE WOODEN SPOONS! FOR COMING LAST IN EVERY COOKERY CONTEST!
WOW! THEY'LL MAKE PERFECT OARS. THANKS, DANNY!
So –
SET SAIL, ME MENACE HEARTIES!
AYE, AYE, CAP'N!
GSLURP! A PIECE OF MEAT PIE-FACE MISSED!
NO, GNASHER! DON'T BITE OUR BOAT'S BOTTOM.
CHOMP!
GNOOPS!
A CAPTAIN ALWAYS GOES DOWN WITH HIS SHIP!
AND THE MENACE CREW!
SORRY, SHIP-MATES!
Back home –
OH, DEAR! GET THOSE WET CLOTHES OFF, BOYS!
THANKS, MUM! WE'RE MUCH WARMER IN THESE TOWELS!
BUT I'VE RUN OUT OF THEM!
WHAT ABOUT ME?
DON'T WORRY, PIE-FACE! I HAVE AN IDEA. I THINK YOU'LL LIKE IT!
OO-ER! I REALLY HAVE TURNED INTO A PIE!
HO-HO! JUST THE THING TO KEEP HIM WARM – A NICE, THICK PIE CRUST!

ANOTHER RUDE WORD YOU CAN GET AWAY WITH!
WHAT? SHE CAN'T SAY THAT!
SSSH!!!!
BOGEY!
PHEW!!!!!
'COURSE ME CAN. ME TOOK FIVE SHOTS INSTEAD OF FOUR! ME GOTTA BOGEY!
BAD LUCK, YOU NICE LITTLE GOLFING GIRLIE!
IT'S TRUE! BOGEY IS A SCORE OF ONE OVER PAR IN GOLF. IT'S A RUDE WORD YOU CAN GET AWAY WITH!
DICTIONARY

A VISIT TO A HEALTH FARM WITH THE SOFTIES

AN UNHEALTHY VISIT TO A FARM WITH THE MENACES!

PESKY JET-SKI

But –
DENNIS. GET YOUR JET-SKI OUT OF MY BATH AT ONCE!
DON'T BE A SPOILSPORT, DAD. IT'S SNOWING OUTSIDE. WE'VE GOT TO JET-SKI SOMEWHERE!
Oh-oh, look at this, readers!
WOW!
GNEEK!
WAAAAH!!!
WHOOSH!
GLUB!
WE'RE FREE!
Mum's friends are around for a cuppa—
GLURPH!
DENNIS!!!!
GLOOP!
SORRY, WE CAN'T STOP TO CHAT, LADIES!
HOI! COME BACK WITH MY TEA TROLLEY, MENACES!
WHEEE!
YIPPEE!
OINKY! I SMELL MESSED-UP GRUB!
OOO!
AAIEE!!!!
GRUNT?

THAT'S LUCKY – THE JET-SKI WORKS ON SNOW.
GNEAT!
HORRID BOY!
SQUEAL!
SIMPER!
THIS IS A GREAT MACHINE FOR MENACING!
OO-ER! I'M NOT SURE ABOUT THIS, THOUGH!
THIS MAY BE A MISTAKE!
GOTTA AGREE!
ZOOM!
BUMP! BOP! WHUMP! BIFF!
OW! OW! OW! IT IS A MISTAKE! OW! OW! ABANDON JET-SKI! OW!
Meanwhile back at the bath–
PEACE AT LAST!
Dennis's voice –
DAD! WE'VE GIVEN UP JET-SKIING!
I'M SO GLAD, DENNIS!
IT'S SCUBA DIVING FROM NOW ON!
OH, NO!!!!!!!
GNASH!
DON'T WORRY, DAD! WE'LL JUST SWIM AROUND FOR A COUPLE OF HOURS, THEN WE'LL LET YOU HAVE YOUR BATH!
SHEESH! I GIVE UP!
SQUALK!
GNASHEE!

GNASHER and GNIPPER
DAD'S GONE TO THE DOGS!
THAT'S TERRIBLE, MUM!
COUSIN ONE EATER FROM SPAIN
GNUH?
SHAME ON YOU, MUM! THAT'S GNOT A GNICE THING TO SAY!
YEAH! JUST BECAUSE HE'S GNOT A GNATTY DRESSER AND HAS LET HIMSELF GO A BIT. GNO GNEED TO SAY HE'S A BIT LIKE US DOGS!
SILLY POOCHES!
NO, LADS. DAD HAS GONE TO THE DOGS. TO THE DOG TRACK – TO WATCH GREYHOUND DOGS RACING!
GNUH-HUH! SOUNDS LIKE FUN!
GNOT HALF! LET'S GO, TOO!
So, at Beanotown greyhound race track–
FINISH
COME ON! COME ON, BABY! YOU CAN DO IT! YOU CAN WIN!
BET
BEANOTOWN GREYHOUND RACE TRACK
GNEE-HEE-HEE! THIS IS COOL! LOOK AT THEM CHASE THE HARE!
ADVANCE! ADVANCE!
GNOW WE SHOULD HAVE A GO!
MOVE ALONG, NOW. QUICKER!!!

The parade for the next race –
GNO WAY WE CAN BEAT THOSE GUYS IN A RACE. THEY'RE GNOT EVEN PUFFED OUT!
GNOTHING TO WORRY ABOUT, GNIPPER. I'LL SEE TO IT IN GNO TIME.
And –
WARNING HEAVY
YOU'LL GNEED GNEW COATS FOR THE RACE, GUYS. IT'S A GNEW RULE! THESE, IN FACT.
DRESSING ROOM
EXHAUSTED!
CLANK! CLANK! CLANK!
COME ALONG, GNOW. RACE TIME!
START
GNEH-HEH! DAD'S GNIFTY IDEA WILL MEAN WE WIN EASILY!
STAGGER!
SQ
MAYBE – BUT LET'S MAKE SURE!
LEAP!
GNEAT – A SCOOTER!

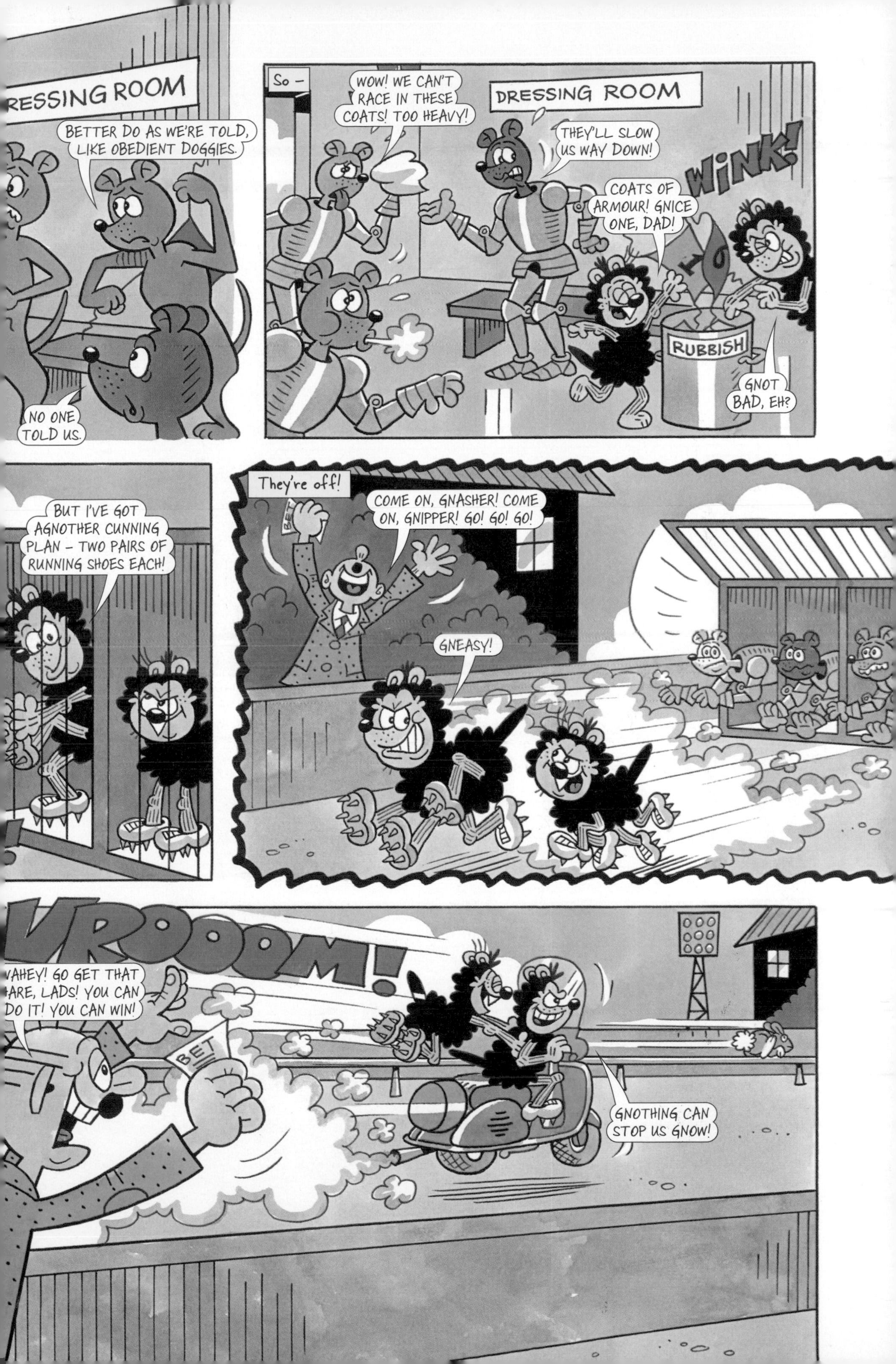

RESSING ROOM
BETTER DO AS WE'RE TOLD, LIKE OBEDIENT DOGGIES.
NO ONE TOLD US.
So –
WOW! WE CAN'T RACE IN THESE COATS! TOO HEAVY!
DRESSING ROOM
THEY'LL SLOW US WAY DOWN!
WINK!
COATS OF ARMOUR! GNICE ONE, DAD!
RUBBISH
GNOT BAD, EH?
BUT I'VE GOT AGNOTHER CUNNING PLAN – TWO PAIRS OF RUNNING SHOES EACH!
They're off!
BET
COME ON, GNASHER! COME ON, GNIPPER! GO! GO! GO!
GNEASY!
VROOOM!
WAHEY! GO GET THAT HARE, LADS! YOU CAN DO IT! YOU CAN WIN!
BET
GNOTHING CAN STOP US GNOW!

VROOOOM!
ALMOST CAUGHT UP WITH THE HARE.
GO GET HIM, SON!
GNEE-HEE!
GNASHER! GNIPPER!
Barry Glennard
SHAME ON YOU TWO - PLAYING WITH A CUDDLY TOY! YOU'RE JUST A COUPLE OF SOFTIES! SNIGGER!
OO-ER! GNOT WHAT IT LOOKS LIKE, DENNIS!
GNO! HOW EMBARRASSING!
PLAYING WITH CUDDLY TOYS - THEY'VE REALLY GONE TO THE DOGS, THOSE MENACES! HA-HA!
ROLL!

YET ANOTHER RUDE WORD YOU CAN GET AWAY WITH!
BLOOMERS!
EEK! YOU CAN'T SAY THAT TO WALTER'S MUMMY!
HOW TERRIBLY EMBARRASSING!
NAW, NAW! BLOOMERS – LOVELY ONES, TOO, IF ME MAY SAY SO!
DOH! WE SEE!
WHY, THANK YOU, YOU LOVELY LITTLE GIRL!
BLOOMERS – BLOOMS THAT BLOOM! HA-HA! ANOTHER RUDE WORD THAT YOU CAN GET AWAY WITH!
DICTION

GNEEEK!
WHAT???? DENNIS COMING OUT OF A CHEMIST'S SHOP WITH LOTS OF SOFTY SMELLY STUFF? CAN'T BE!!!
DON'T WORRY, MENACING MATES! ALL THESE SOPPY SMELLY THINGS ARE JUST WHAT I NEED FOR SOME MENACING MOMENTS!
SHAMPOO
SPRAY!
I'M NOT ALLOWED A BOTTLE OFCHAMPAGNE LIKE THOSE RACING DRIVERS. SHAKING A BOTTLE OF SHAMPOO WORKS JUST AS WELL, THOUGH!
SPLURT!
SHAMPOO
SHRIEK!
SOAKED!
THOROUGHLY!
TALCUM POWDER
OOO! THE DUST! THE DUST! AND I'VE JUST FEATHER DUSTED MY WENDY HOUSE! COFF! COFF!
HAW-HAW!
TALC
COFF! COFF! SPLUTTER!

HAIR GEL
EXTRA-STRONG HAIR GEL
SHAKE!
WAFT! WAFT!
GENTLEST BREEZE!
STIFF HAIR MEANS I CAN BLOW WALTER RIGHT OFF HIS FEET!
OO! SUCH A STRONG BLAST!
INTO MY YUKKY BROWN STUFF!
MOISTURISER
I SAY! WHO DROPPED THAT?
OH, NO! NOT WHAT YOU THINK, VICAR!
HA-HA! RUBBING MOISTURISER INTO YOUR HANDS SOUNDS GREAT!
RASP!
SQUINK!
THRRP!
PRRRPP!
RAASSP!!
SHAVING FOAM
WAHEY! A SNOW WALTER!
FSS!
SHAVING FOAM
LEMME OUT! I'M TRAPPED IN A SHAVING FOAM COCOON!
FSS!
AFTER SHAVE
SEE? SMELLY TOILETRIES CAN COME IN HANDY – LIKE WHEN YOUR BEST PAL FAINTS. IT BRINGS HIM ROUND!
GNEH? WH-WH-? LAST THING I REMEMBER IS THE MENACE WITH SOFTY STUFF!
Blue Strathclyde AFTER SHAVE

DENNIS'S DAY OUT!
YIPPEE! WE CAN GET AWAY WITH ANY KIND OF MENACING TODAY!
Dennis's sleeping little sister Bea. SSSSH!!!!....
GNEE-HEE!

3...2...1...
...JUMP!
LEAP!
LEAP!
WHA....WHO...WH ERE....WH...
SPIN!
AND SPIN! HAW-HAW!
WHEEE!
GRRR!!! MENACES!
THAT'S US, ALL RIGHT! LET'S MOVE ON, GNASHER!
WHAT'S GNEXT?
CLIMB ABOARD, PAL!
SUPERMARKET
ZOOM!
YIKES!
PESTS!
SCREECH!
CRASH!
OOOOOOO!!!!
WAHEY!
BASH!
SWERVE!
SUPERMARKET
YES! TWO MINUTES EXACTLY! A NEW SHOP LAP RECORD!
WE ARE THE CHAMPIONS!
MENACES!
NEDS!
SUPERMARKET
'OOLIGANS!
THEY'RE OFF THEIR TROLLIES!

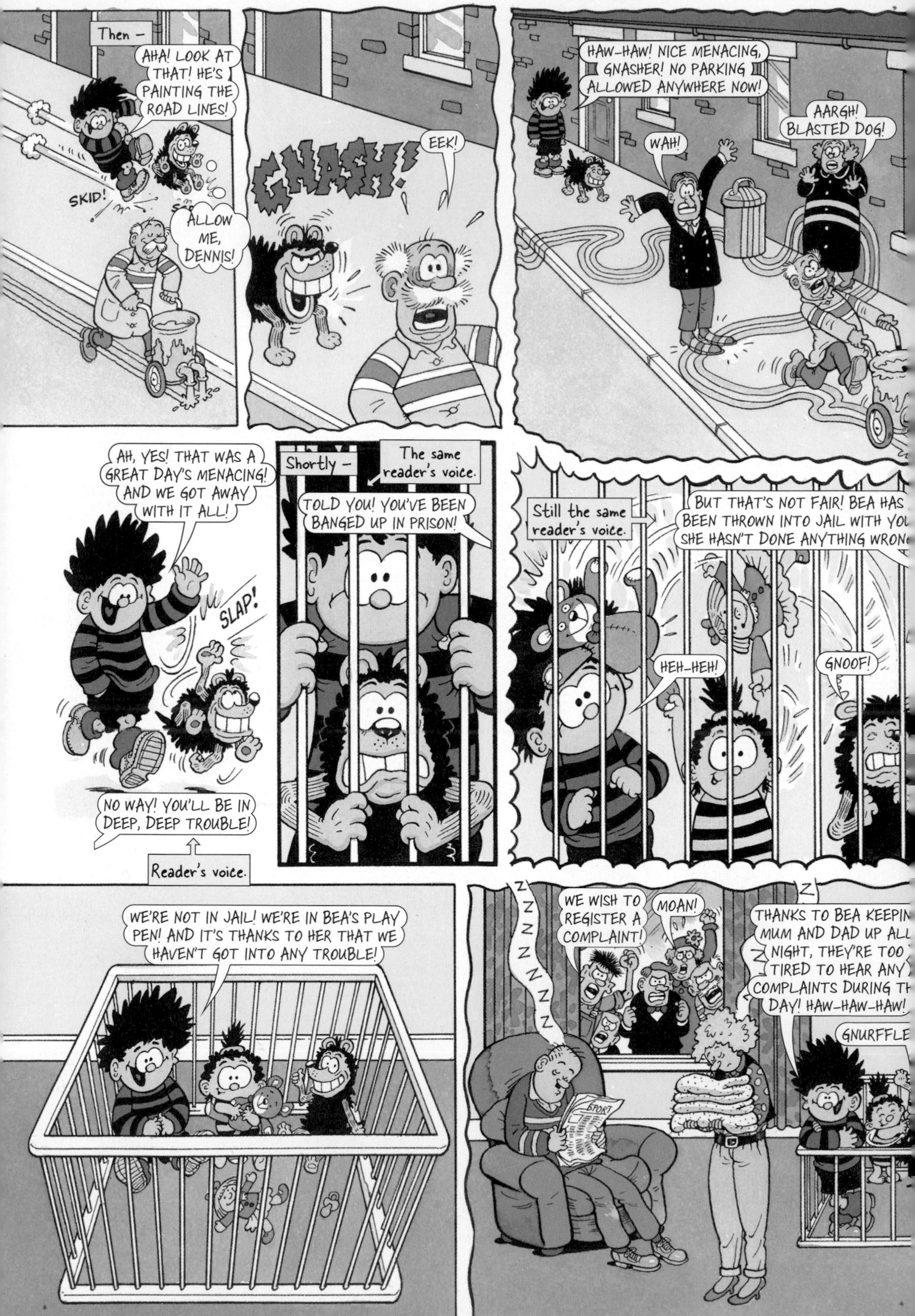
Then –
AHA! LOOK AT THAT! HE'S PAINTING THE ROAD LINES!
SKID!
ALLOW ME, DENNIS!
GNASH!
EEK!
HAW-HAW! NICE MENACING, GNASHER! NO PARKING ALLOWED ANYWHERE NOW!
WAH!
AARGH! BLASTED DOG!
AH, YES! THAT WAS A GREAT DAY'S MENACING! AND WE GOT AWAY WITH IT ALL!
SLAP!
NO WAY! YOU'LL BE IN DEEP, DEEP TROUBLE!
Reader's voice.
Shortly –
The same reader's voice.
TOLD YOU! YOU'VE BEEN BANGED UP IN PRISON!
Still the same reader's voice.
BUT THAT'S NOT FAIR! BEA HAS BEEN THROWN INTO JAIL WITH YOU SHE HASN'T DONE ANYTHING WRONG
HEH-HEH!
GNOOF!
WE'RE NOT IN JAIL! WE'RE IN BEA'S PLAY PEN! AND IT'S THANKS TO HER THAT WE HAVEN'T GOT INTO ANY TROUBLE!
WE WISH TO REGISTER A COMPLAINT!
MOAN!
THANKS TO BEA KEEPIN MUM AND DAD UP ALL NIGHT, THEY'RE TOO TIRED TO HEAR ANY COMPLAINTS DURING TH DAY! HAW-HAW-HAW!
GNURFFLE
SPORT

ABRA KEBAB RA
with
DENNIS the MENACE
and GNASHER
SHISH KEBAB FOR YOU, CURLY. KOFTE KEBAB FOR YOU, PIE FACE. AND WHOSE ARE THE DONERS?
STEAM!
SLURP!
SIZZLE!
GIMME. GIMME!
GSLOBBER!
DONERS? THAT'S US. WE'LL TAKE THE DONER KEBABS!

YUP! WE'RE THE DONERS, ALL RIGHT! WE LOVE DONER KEBABS!
YOU BET!
DONORS, DID YOU SAY? WHY, THAT'S SO NICE OF YOU!
TOWN HALL
DONORS THIS WAY. BLOOD DONORS, THAT IS!
BLOOD DONORS WANTED
WELL, THIS WAY, THEN! I'M HELPING MUMMY TODAY.
EH? WHY? WHAT'S GOING ON?
CHOMP
GENTLE PUSH
WOW! THAT KIND OF DONORS! THIS IS A FAB MENACING OPPORTUNITY, IF I'M NOT MISTAKEN!
HOW BRAVE YOU ARE.
OO! YOU'VE EMPTIED ME, WALTER'S MUM!
GNEAT!
LET'S MENACE!
NO! NO! DONATE! DO NOT MENACE!
TOSS
TOSS
DASH!

WARRGHH!! SLIPPERY GREASY KEBAB WRAPPER!!!
WHEE!
SLIP!
GIVE BLOOD
TIME TO DONATE, PALS!
SPLAT
GIVE
ROLL UP YOUR SLEEVE!
DON'T BE SILLY. IT'S A BAGUETTE UP MY SLEEVE, NOT A ROLL.
YEUCCH!! CHEESY AND NIFFY!
OO! NEXT DONOR, ROLL UP YOUR SLEEVE.
GNO!
SHRIEEKUMS!!!!
GNO ROLLS UP MY SLEEVE - JUST FLEAS! GNEE-HEE-HEE!
LEAP!
BUMP!

WE SHOULD BE ABLE TO FIND SOME NEW DONORS IN HERE, GNASHER!
BASH St. SCHOOL
GHUH?
THAT'S RIGHT, GNASHER. IF YOU DONATE BLOOD, YOU GET A FREE CUP OF TEA. AND A BISCUIT!
GHUH?
DRIB
DID SOME ON
SAY FREE TE
TEACH
A GOAL
FOR THE
THAT'S RIGHT, FREE TEA AND BICCYS! TELL ALL THE TEACHERS AND HEAD—MASTERS YOU KNOW!
FREE TEA! AND BICCYS! PASS IT ON!
Soon, there are hundrds of donors. All Teachers and Headmasters.
GIVE BLOOD
COFFEE AND BISCUITS HERE
COFF
YOU'VE FOUND LOTS OF DONORS. THIS IS SO NICE OF YOU, DENNIS.
NICE? NO WAY. WE'RE MENACES AND WE'RE HUNGRY!
GNESH!

AND BICCYS? I HEARD SOME ONE MENTION BICCYS!
INK
THUD!
YUP!
BOOT!
WELL, THAT'S FOR US!
LET'S GO!
BURST!
SQUASH!
SO WE'LL FINISH OFF OUR SIX HOUR OLD COLD KEBABS! DELISH!
OO! HOW COULD I HAVE THOUGHT THE MENACES WOULD EVER BE NICE? I FEEL SO SICK!
FAINT
STOMACH PUMP READY!
STALE ODOUR
NASTY NIFF!
GNICE!
BOKE!
PUMP
COLD GREASY PONG

SPREAD THE WORD
BEANO
GNUH? A SPREAD ABOUT SPREADS!
SPREAD EAGLE
THE SPREAD EAGLE
I LOVE CHEESE SPREAD, ME! GONNA LICK IT ALL OFF HIM!
SILLY SOFTY! THAT'S A SPREAD EAGLE!
WHIMPER!
MIDDLE AGED SPREAD
COR! I THINK SHE LIKES ME!
NOT IF YOU LET HER SEE YOUR MIDDLE AGED SPREAD, DAD!
A WOBBLY BELLY! YUK!
MUCK SPREADER
3000 GALLONS PIG MUD
GRR! THOSE MENACES HAVE GONE TOO FAR!

CHEESE SPREAD
WAH! YOU'RE SUPPOSED TO SPREAD THE CHEESE SPREAD ON BREAD, NOT MY HEAD!
I CAN'T CONCEIVE IT AIN'T CHEESE
REALLY, SOFTY?
SPREADSHEET
SPREADSHEETS ARE WHAT MUM USES ON HER COMPUTER. DON'T THINK BEA HAS GOT THE RIGHT IDEA!
ME'S SPREAD ME'S SHEET FER A PICKY-NICK!
DAD'S COMPOST HEAP
NICE AND STINKY
NIGEL PARKINSON
SPREAD 'EM
SPREAD 'EM, MENACES! I'M TAKING YOU IN FOR SPREADING MISERY TO ALL THESE NICE PEOPLE!
TIME FOR ONE LAST SPREAD!

ROCK-A-BYE
BAY-BEA!
SIGH! BEA JUST WON'T TAKE HER AFTERNOON NAP!
WAAAAA!
OOO!
WOW! I HAVEN'T HEARD SO MUCH BAWLING SINCE I PUT ICE CREAM DOWN SOFTY WALTER'S SHORTS!
GNOUCH!

TAKE BEA OUT FOR A WALK IN HER PRAM, DENNIS. THE ROCKING MIGHT PUT HER TO SLEEP.
WAAAAAA!!!
SURE, MUM!
BUT I'VE GOT A BETTER IDEA, GNASHER.
WAAAA!
WE'LL TAKE BEA OUT...
WAA!
CLICK!
VROOOM!
...IN THE MENACE CAR. IT REALLY ROCKS!
I KNOW JUST THE THINGS TO PUT BEA TO SLEEP.
GNEH?
THEY SHOULD BE IN HERE.
GNUH?
SHEEP, I MEAN! COUNTING SHEEP IS MEANT TO MAKE ANYONE SLEEP. PITY THERE'S NO SHEEP. JUST COWS.
FREEDOM!
LET'S SCARPER!
ESCAPING COWS, AT THAT!
HOI! CATTLE! DON'T GET OFF MOI LAND!
THE FARMER! TIME FOR US TO SCARPER!
WE'LL LEAVE HIM COUNTING THE COWS. I HAVE ANOTHER IDEA.
ARR! MENACES!

WATCHING FISH IN AN AQUARIUM IS ALSO SUPPOSED TO BE RELAXING.
BOATING LAKE
BUT I DON'T KNOW WHERE OUR NEAREST AQUARIUM IS. SO...
YIKES!
MENACE TORPEDO!!!
...WE'LL HAVE TO GO TO FIND THE FISH AT HOME!
But –
'EM'S FUNNY LOOKIN' FISHYS!
BAH! NO FISH AROUND AND BEA IS STILL AWAKE! TIME TO GO.
SPLASH!
WAHEY!
WAH! MENACE SURFACE TO AIR MISSILE!
SPLOSH!
YIKES AGAIN!
Shortly –
ZZZZZZ!!!
AH! BEA HAS FALLEN ASLEEP AT LAST!
MUM AND DAD WILL BE PLEASED WITH US FOR ONCE.
They are!
GOOD WORK, YOU TWO! HAVE A TREAT!
THANKS, KIND PARENTS!
But –
OI! MENACES! WE WANT A WORD!
GRR!
SNARL!
WHAT DO YOU MEAN MY NICE BOY AND HIS D
CAUSED ALL THESE PROBLEMS? THEY ONLY
THEIR LITTLE SISTER FOR A WALK! HOW COUL
THEY CAUSE ANY PROBLEMS DOING THAT?
EASY, WHEN YOU'RE A MENACE!
GNEE-HEE!

GOING BANANAS!
YAHOO! WE'RE OFF TO VISIT OUR FAVOURITE INMATE!
OTOWN ZOO

THAT'S HUGO THE GORILLA!
SIGH!
FANCY A BITE TO EAT, HUGO?
GNICE 'NANAS!
STOPPIT! STOPPIT!
EH? WHAT'S WRONG WITH HIM?
POP! POP! POP!
SQUEEZE!
GORILLAS ARE MEANT TO BE TOUGH AND STRONG, NOT WIMPY AS A SOFTY! SHOW ME YOU'RE TOUGH ENOUGH – THUMP YOUR CHEST AND HOLLER LIKE A REAL GORILLA!
VERY WELL, THEN. IF I MUST!
PIT!
PAT!
OOYAH! OOYAH! THAT HURT! ME POOR OLD CHEST THROBS! AND I HURT MY LIKKLE FINGERS!
POOR HUGO! I THINK HE'S GONE SOFT BECAUSE HE HASN'T BEEN IN THE WILD FOR SO LONG!
GNOT FAIR!
ANTI-BRUISE OINTMENT
WE'LL HAVE TO TEACH YOU HOW TO BE TOUGH AGAIN! FIRST....
...GET HIM OUT OF THERE, GNASHER!
GNZZZZZ!
OO! DO I HAVE TO? REALLY?
C'MON, HUGO!
PICK!

OVELY DAY FOR A TEA PARTY!
PASS THE PROFITEROLES, PLEASE!
THAT'S IT, HUGO! GET STUCK INTO THE SOFTY PICNIC! HA-HA!
YEEK!
MUMMY!
OH, NO! HUGO IS WORSE THAN WE THOUGHT!
COO! HE JUST WANTS TO JOIN US!
I DO LIKE A NICE CUPPA!
Meanwhile—
I'LL JUST PINCH A READ OF DENNIS'S BEANO BEFORE I DELIVER IT TO HIM.
COO-EE!
AAARGHHH!!!! A G-G-G-GORILLA!
OOPS!
SPLUNGE!
ER, I'M AFRAID I'VE DAMAGED YOUR BEANO A LITTLE, DENNIS!
MY BEANO???????????
GRAAAAGHHH!!!!....
SO THAT'S HOW IT'S DONE.
THUMP!
R-R-RIP!
THUMP! THUMP!
GRAAAGHHH!!!!....
THUMP!
WAHEY! I THINK HUGO HAS THE IDEA AT LAST!
WELL, I'M PROUD TO SAY THAT HUGO ISN'T A SOFTY ANY MORE.
IN FACT, HE'S A PROPER MENACE!
KEEPER
SPLOT!
WAH! HE WAS NEVER LIKE THIS BEFORE – 'TILL DENNIS VISITED!

YES — ANOTHER RUDE WORD YOU CAN GET AWAY WITH!
NO! NOT HERE!
DON'T!
POOP!
POOP! NOTTA SMELLY ONE!
POOP DECK
PHEW! SHE WASN'T GOING TO AFTER ALL!
WHAT A RELIEF!
POOP DECK – THE AFTER PART OF A SHIP, A HIGH DECK AT THE STERN! SNIGGER! CRAFTY ONE, THAT! BUT IT'S ANOTHER RUDE WORD YOU CAN GET AWAY WITH!
HMS VICTORY

OFF HER ROCKER!

BEA JUST LOVES HER ROCKING HORSE.
DIS HORSIE AIN'T GOIN' ANYWHERE.
ROCK!
OOPS! TOO MUCH ROCKIN'!
ME'S GOIN' SOMEWHERE NOW. GIZZA LIFT ON YER BACK, BIG BRUVVER!
SORRY, LITTLE BEA. IT'S NOT SAF FOR YOU TO GO T SOME OF THE PLACES A MENAC LIKE ME GOES.
AWW! FUDDY DUDDY!
ME'S NOT STAYIN' IN.
NOW WHAT IS SHE UP TO?
OH-OH! GNASHER WON'T LIKE THIS!
ME'S SADDLIN' UP ME'S NEW TRUSTY STEED!
FLONK!
GIDDYUP, HORSIE!
LEAP!
TUG!
SO IT'S GIDDYUP YOU WANT, IS IT? OK.
OOOH!!!
HA-HA! HANG ON, BEA!
EEEKUMS!
GNA-HA!
SPIN!
WAAAH!
ZOOM!

OON –
GNASP! GNEED A DRINK!
PUFF! PANT!
HAW-HAW! BAD LUCK, BEA!
GSLURP!
GLOOP!
HOW D'YOU LIKE YOUR EARLY BATH, BEA?
AGAIN! AGAIN! DAT WAS FUN! ANOVVER GO, GNASHER!
CLAP!
GNUH?
HAVE SOME SWEETS, LOVELY LITTLE GRAND CHILD!
GRANNY!
AND –
ME LOVES YER SWEETIES!
STRONG MINTS
OO! BURNY HOT!
PTOO!
MIBBEE HORSEY LIKES 'EM BETTER! HAVE A NOSE BAG!
STRONG MINTS
GNASH! GNASH!
SEE, GNASHER? BEA'S NOT SO BAD AFTER ALL!
STRONG MINTS
MUNCH! CRUNCH!
AND IF YOU THOUGHT THAT WAS FUN, READERS, HAVE A LOOK AT WHAT BEA GETS UP TO WITH HER OTHER TOYS – OVER THE PAGE!
C'MON, BRUVVER! WE'S GOT MENACIN' TO DO!

BEA'S BITS 'N' BOBS
SOME KIDS USE ALL THAT KIDDY STUFF. BUT MY LITTLE SIS ISN'T JUST ANY KID.
GNEE-HEE! SEE HOW SHE PLAYS WITH KIDS STUFF!
A CHUTE
SIMPLY SUPER SLIPPY FUN!
SLIDE!
WAHEY! ME'S GOT ME'S OWN PARA-CHUTE!
COR!
A MOBILE
VROOOOOOOM!
ROA
HUKKA!
ME USES ME'S MOBILE T'ORDER LOTSA PIZZAS! YUMMY!
OO! ME CAN'T SLEEP NOW!
PIZZA PIZZA
LOVELY MOBILE HELPS ME TO GO TO SLEEP!

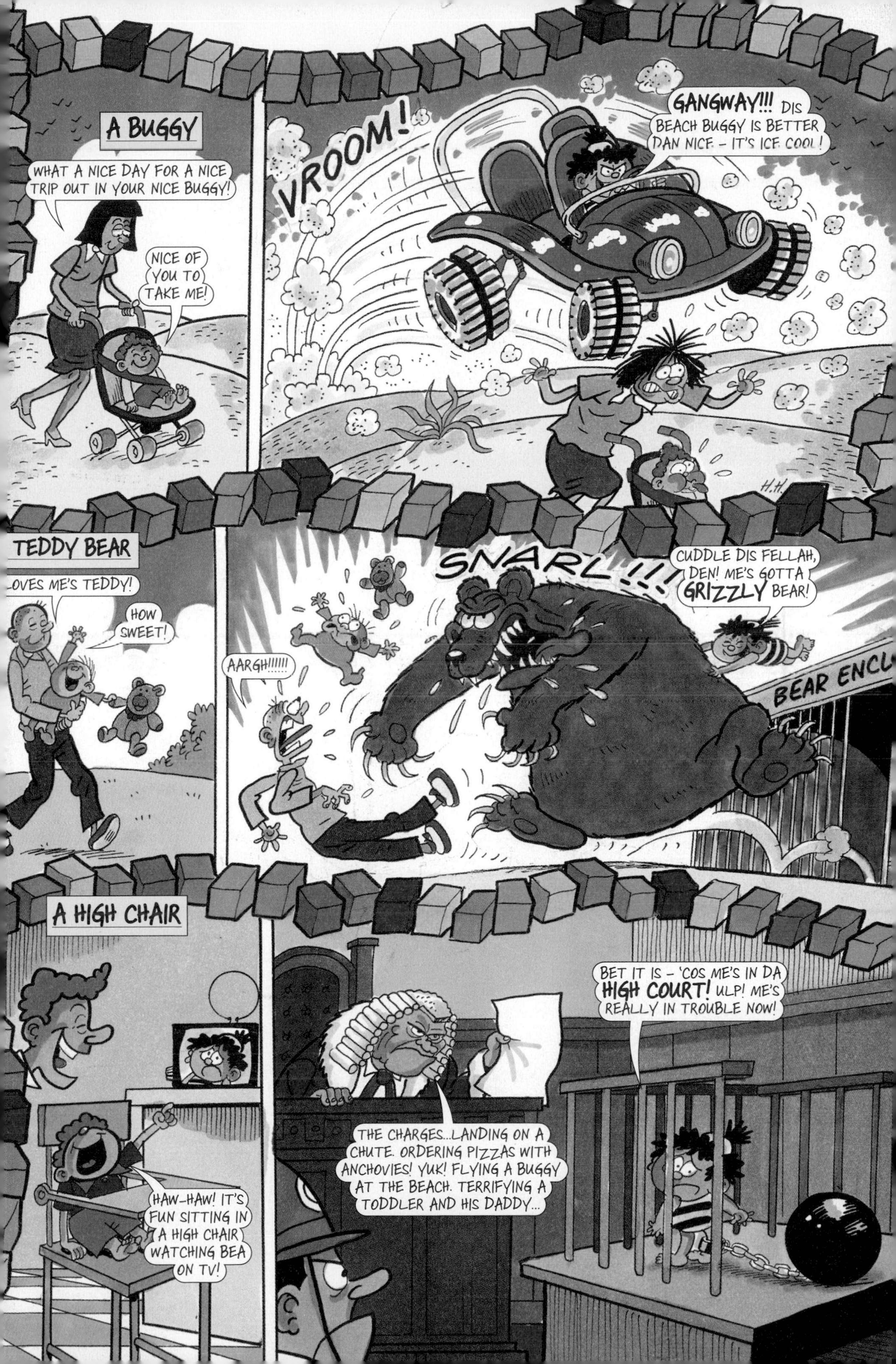

A BUGGY
WHAT A NICE DAY FOR A NICE TRIP OUT IN YOUR NICE BUGGY!
NICE OF YOU TO TAKE ME!
VROOM!
GANGWAY!!! DIS BEACH BUGGY IS BETTER DAN NICE – IT'S ICE COOL!
H.H.
TEDDY BEAR
LOVES ME'S TEDDY!
HOW SWEET!
SNARL!!!
CUDDLE DIS FELLAH, DEN! ME'S GOTTA GRIZZLY BEAR!
AARGH!!!!!!
BEAR ENCL
A HIGH CHAIR
HAW-HAW! IT'S FUN SITTING IN A HIGH CHAIR WATCHING BEA ON TV!
THE CHARGES...LANDING ON A CHUTE. ORDERING PIZZAS WITH ANCHOVIES! YUK! FLYING A BUGGY AT THE BEACH. TERRIFYING A TODDLER AND HIS DADDY...
BET IT IS – 'COS ME'S IN DA HIGH COURT! ULP! ME'S REALLY IN TROUBLE NOW!

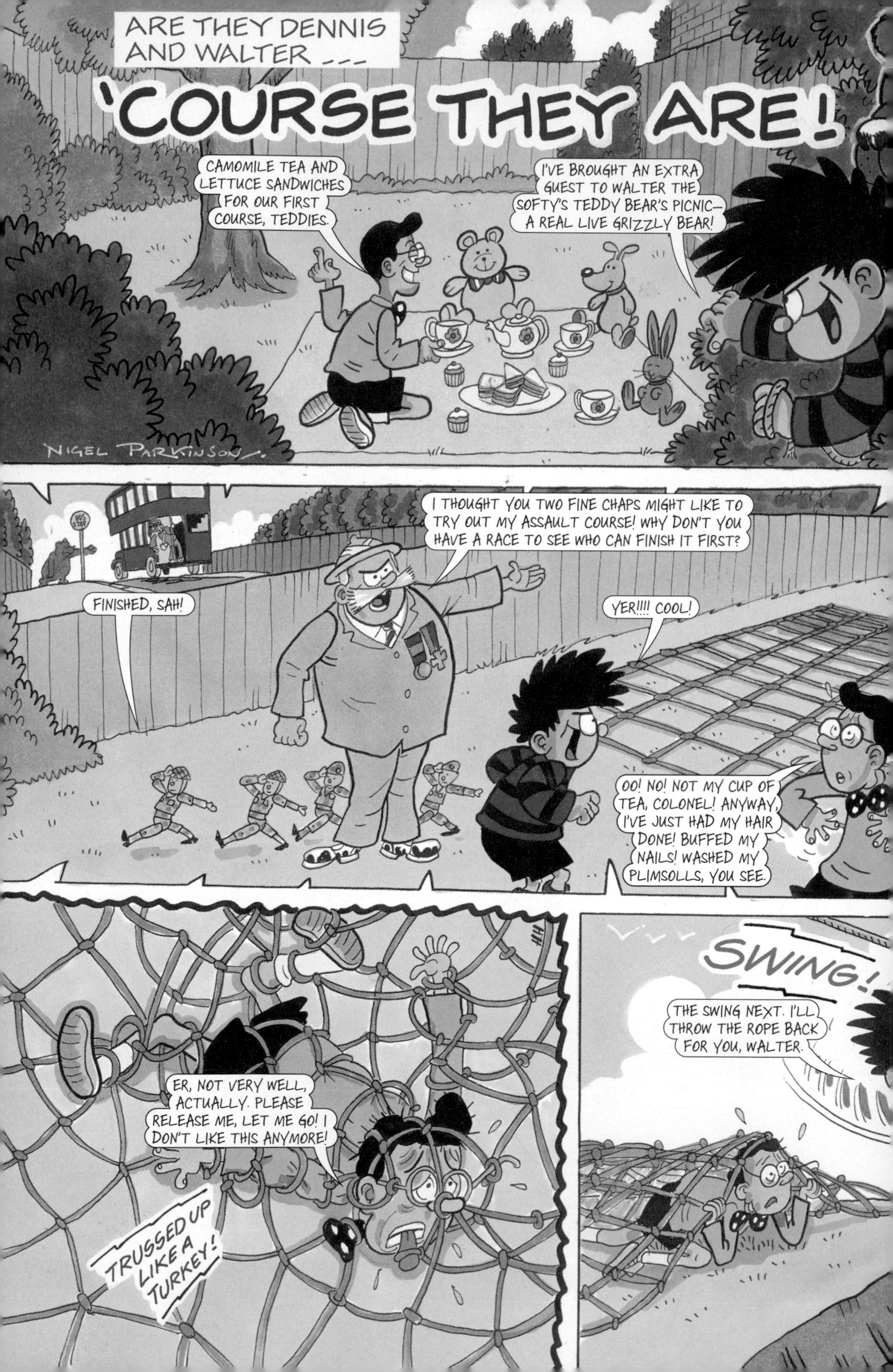

ARE THEY DENNIS AND WALTER ...
'COURSE THEY ARE!
CAMOMILE TEA AND LETTUCE SANDWICHES FOR OUR FIRST COURSE, TEDDIES.
I'VE BROUGHT AN EXTRA GUEST TO WALTER THE SOFTY'S TEDDY BEAR'S PICNIC— A REAL LIVE GRIZZLY BEAR!
NIGEL PARKINSON
BUS STOP
I THOUGHT YOU TWO FINE CHAPS MIGHT LIKE TO TRY OUT MY ASSAULT COURSE! WHY DON'T YOU HAVE A RACE TO SEE WHO CAN FINISH IT FIRST?
FINISHED, SAH!
YER!!!! COOL!
OO! NO! NOT MY CUP OF TEA, COLONEL! ANYWAY, I'VE JUST HAD MY HAIR DONE! BUFFED MY NAILS! WASHED MY PLIMSOLLS, YOU SEE.
ER, NOT VERY WELL, ACTUALLY. PLEASE RELEASE ME, LET ME GO! I DON'T LIKE THIS ANYMORE!
TRUSSED UP LIKE A TURKEY!
SWING!
THE SWING NEXT. I'LL THROW THE ROPE BACK FOR YOU, WALTER.

ON LOAN FROM BEANOTOWN ZOO
A HUNGRY GRIZZLY, ME!
Suddenly –
HUP! TWO! THREE! FOUR!
WOW! WHAT'S GOING ON, COLONEL?
MY PLATOON OF ROYAL ENGINEERS ARE BUILDING ME MY VERY OWN ASSAULT COURSE. JOLLY DECENT OF THEM, DON'T YOU KNOW?
GNASH!
GNASH!
GNASH!
SQUEAL!!!!
THAT'S IT, GNASHER, GIVE WALTER SOME 'ENCOURAGEMENT'!
SCRAMBLE!
THE NETS ARE EASY! CAN'T WAIT TO SEE HOW THE SOFT BOY GOT ON.
WHIMPER! WHAT A BLAST!
PATHETIC LITTLE GUST!
WIMP! THE WIND FROM THE ROPE HAS BLOWN HIM OVER!
THE BALANCE BEAM – AN OLD TREE TRUNK! NO PROBS!

UNLESS THIS HAPPENS, OF COURSE! HA-HA!
BOOT!
BLATTER!
WAHHH!! I'M AIRBORNE!
WELL, NO, YOU WON'T! I FORGOT TO PUT ON SOME DEODORANT THIS MORNING! AGAIN!
SWEATY NIFF!
GAG! GUFF! GROO! FAINT!
POW!
Finally –
THE BIG FINISH! COME ON UP, WALTER!
NO WAY! NOT A CHANCE! NOT ME!
WHOOSH-
THE DEATH SLIDE! YIPPEEEEEEEE!!!!
VERY IMPRESSIVE, YOUNG SOLDIER!
SOFTY FAINT!

SPLURF!
NO, WALTER. YOU'RE BACK ON SOLID GROUND. WELL, THERE'S NOTHING SOLID IN THERE!
COLONEL'S COMPOST HEAP (OOH! STINKY!!)
THE HANGING BARS. YOU'LL LIKE THESE, WALTER.
I WILL?
A SPLASH OF WATER FROM THE WATER OBSTACLE WILL BRING HIM ROUND.
SPLASH!
It does!
TOLD YOU, READERS! THE PRINCE OF SOFTIES DOESN'T LIKE HAVING HIS JERSEY SPLASHED!
LOOK AT THIS! A SPLASH! ON MY NEWLY DRY CLEANED CHEMISE! IT'S RUINED! PURE ANGORA, THIS! SMUDGED! I CAN'T WEAR THIS AGAIN! WHAT WILL MY FRIENDS IN DRESSMAKING CLASS THINK?
YAHEY! I WIN! DON'T THINK THE SOFT ONE WILL FINISH YOUR ASSAULT COURSE, COLONEL!
DOESN'T LOOK LIKELY! WELL DONE, DENNIS!
YES, WELL DONE, DENNIS. BUT PERHAPS YOU'D LIKE TO TRY OUT OUR ASSAULT COURSE. THE ONE WE'VE BUILT FOR WALTER!
EH? WHO ARE YOU LOT?

THE HOUSEHOLD CAVALRY! QUEEN'S OWN! WE'VE BUILT A SOFTY ASSAULT COURSE! BET YOU CAN'T BEAT WALTER AROUND IT!
WHAT? DID SOMEONE MENTION MY NAME?
BAH! SOFTY SMELLY THING! HOW DOES IT WORK? HOW DO I GET OUT?
NEXT, THE BALANCE BEAM. WELL, US SOFTIES HAVE TO BALANCE ON THESE TREMENDOUSLY HIGH HEELS. TRY IT, MENACE! IF YOU DARE!
GAG! GUFF! GROO!
FLOWERY FUMES!
SWEET SMELL!
NO WATER OBSTACLES FOR SOFTIES. WE HAVE WATER FEATURES! FULL OF ROSE WATER! PERFECT FOR DABBING BEHIND THE EARS!

OO! MY OWN ASSAULT COURSE! HOW SIMPLY SPIFFING! CHASE ME DENNIS!
SKIPPITY SKIP!
SURE! I'LL BEAT YOU ROUND BOTH ASSAULT COURSES, SOFTY!
FIRST OBSTACLE IS QUITE LIKE THOSE NETS, BUT A SOFTY VERSION – A DUVET. GOT TO GIVE IT A GOOD AIRING!
SNUGGLE-DOWN LOVELY WARM DUVET
A WHAT?
WARGHHH!! CAN'T STAND THIS! CAN'T STAND AT ALL!
TEE-HEE! NOT AS EASY AS IT LOOKS, IS IT?
HANGING BARS? NOT FOR US SOFTY CHAPS. WE HAVE HANGING BASKETS! CHECK OUT MY PETUNIAS.
WHAT A NIFF!
WE END WITH A SLIDE, TOO! THIS IS THE BEST WAY TO POLISH THE LINOLEUM FLOOR COVERING! LOVELY SHINE!
NO WAY AM I DOING THAT!
SLIDE!
SLIDE!

WELL, YOU HAVE WON ONE COURSE EACH! TIME FOR A THIRD, DECIDING COURSE!
GRR! I'LL WIN IT!
NO, I WILL!
THE DESSERT COURSE! TUCK IN, BOYS! YOU MUST BE HUNGRY AFTER ALL THAT RUNNING ABOUT!
ICES
YEAH! THANKS, COLONEL!
YIPPEE! SCRUMPTIOUS!

ALMOST THE LAST RUDE WORD YOU CAN GET AWAY WITH!
SNOTTER!
SHE'S GONE TOO FAR!
OO! THE SHAME OF HAVING A RUDE-MOUTHED DAUGHTER!
NOT AT ALL, PARENTS! DAT'S A SNOTTER THERE! IT'SA FITTING DAT HOLDS THE HEEL OF A SPRIT. AN' A SPRIT ISSA SPAR SET TO EXTEND A SAIL! TROO!
SEE? ANOTHER RUDE WORD YOU CAN GET AWAY WITH!
AR! SHE BE RIGHT!
DICTIO

NOT REMOTELY CONTROLLED!
THAT BOY OF YOURS – AND HIS DOG – ARE OUT OF CONTROL!
ANOTHER DENNIS VICTIM!
MEET THE MENACES!

DENNIS! PLEASE! YOU MUST LEARN TO CONTROL YOURSELF. AND YOU, TOO, GNASHER!
MOAN! WHINGE!
BUT WE CAN'T, DAD!
OF COURSE YOU CAN CONTROL YOURSELF, DENNIS. NOW HAVE A DRINK AND SETTLE DOWN.
HUMPH!
OH, NO! MY HANDS! I CAN'T CONTROL THEM!
FIZZ
OR MY FINGERS! DON'T DO IT! STOP!
FIZZ
YOU'RE RIGHT, DAD! I'M OUT OF CONTROL!
WARGHHH!!! GLOPSH!!
SWOOSH!
FSST!
NAUGHTY, NAUGHTY HANDS! YOU SHOULDN'T HAVE DONE THAT FINE PIECE OF MENACING!
SOON –
AND GNASHER CAN'T CONTROL HIS GNASHERS WHEN HE'S NEAR A MOGGY!
RASP!
GNASH! GNASH!
WHICH IS HANDY FOR GETTING RID OF OLD BRANCHES.
AND THE OCCASIONAL SILLY STATUE – DAD'S FAVE!
GREEK GOD OF GRUMPINESS
OH, NO! NOW MY LEG IS OUT OF CONTROL. IT'S GOT A MIND OF ITS OWN!
TWITCH! TWITCH!

DON'T DO IT, FOOT! DON'T!
COOOEE! HELLO, LITTLE FISHY-WISHY-WISHY!
TUT-TUT! BAD FOOT DIDN'T LISTEN TO ME!
PUSH!
GSNIGGER!
WE REALLY CAN'T CONTROL OURSELVES NOW! HAR-HAR-HAR!
GNEE-HEE!!!!!
SPLORP!
MENACES! I KNOW YOU WERE FIBBING ABOUT NOT BEING ABLE TO CONTROL YOURSELVES!
CAUGHT!
SIT THERE AND LISTEN TO SOME NICE, SOOTHING MUSIC WITH ME!
SOUNDS AWFUL!
AND NOW, A ROCK 'N' ROLL MEDLEY!
PSST! WATCH WHAT HAPPENS NOW, GNASHER
VOL
WE'RE GONNA ROCK ARO THE CLOC
FIDGET!
TWIDDLE!
TAP! TAP!
COOL!
AHA!
I KNEW THESE TWO COULDN'T CONTROL THEMSELVES WHEN THEY HEARD THIS OLD FASHIONED MUSIC! THEY LISTENED TO THIS WHEN THEY WERE DATING!
ROCK ROCK ROCK..
SWING IT, DADDY - O!
TSK! TSK! NO WONDER DENNIS AND GNASHER CAN'T CONTROL THEMSELVES WITH THOSE PARENTS AS AN EXAMPLE!
SHOCKING BEHAVIOUR!
BOGEY!
BOOGIE!

DO US A FAVOUR!

POOR GNASHER? NO WAY! I'M DOING HIM A FAVOUR – HELPING HIM UP INTO THAT TREE.
GNASH!
WHIMPER!
HO-HO! I SEE!
GNASH! GNASH!
MEOWL!#&!^*~*#)*!
NOW HE CAN CATCH THAT CAT!
AND HE'S DOING ME A FAVOUR!
OW! APPLES!
WE LIKE TO DO EACH OTHER FAVOURS. READY, GNASHER?
GOTCHA!
BUT –
POYOING!
LOOKS LIKE I'VE DONE GNASHER ANOTHER FAVOUR!
AARGH!!!
GYUMMY!
BUTCHER
AA...OOO.....GET OUT OF THERE, YOU GREEDY GNASHER!
THIS FAVOUR HAS LOTS OF FLAVOUR!
BUTCHER

WASHER IS DOING ME ANOTHER FAVOUR.
'S THAT, DENNIS?
EXAM PAPER
WAH!
SQUEAL!
DENNIS'S TEACHER!
ONE OF THOSE EXAM PAPERS IS MINE, AND NOW IT'S GONE! WAHEY! WHAT A SHAME! CHORTLE!
COME BACK!
?
EXAM PAPER
GRAND OPENING TODAY BOUNCY TEDDY
WIMPORIUM
SAILOR SUITS
LOOK TEDDY CLOTHES
ASBESTOS GLOVES FOR PICKING UP SOFT BOILED EGGS
SAFETY NETS (for high beds)
WASHED COAL
LULLABY TAPES
JOLLY FUN! WHAT A SIMPLY SOOPER NEW SHOP OPENING TODAY!
EXAM PAPER
BUT THAT POOR LITTLE BIRDIE CAN'T SEE WHERE IT'S GOING!
POP!
FISSSSS
OH-OH!
FLUMP!
SSSSSSS!
SQUEAL! ATTACKED BY A DEFLATING TEDDY!
WELL DONE, BIRD! YOU DESERVE A BIG FAVOUR FROM US FOR FLATTENING THE SOFT BOYS!
SIMPER!
SO WE'VE MADE YOU A SPECIAL SANDWICH! TUCK IN!
WOW! WORMS!
GROO! DO US A FAVOUR – GIVE US BLINDFOLDS! QUICKLY!

SNACK ATTACK
MORE SANDWICH SILLINESS
CHEESE SANDWICH
TUCK IN, WALTER! THE CHEESY BITS ARE VERY MATURE!
GROO! EEE-YUK!
CHEESY SOCK GUFF!
HAM SANDWICH
OOOO! GET THESE PORKERS AWAY FROM ME!
SQUASH!
RASHER'S PIGGY PAL, PIGGY STARDUST.
HEE-HEE! WALTER'S SANDWICHED BY TWO PRIME HAM HUNKS!
NIGEL PARKINSON
PEANUT BUTTER SANDWICH
HAVE A PEANUT BUTTER SANDWICH, OLD PAL. ON ME!
SPLARF!
SQUARF!
ON ME, MORE LIKE! WHIMPER!

STEAK SANDWICH
PAIN!
CRUNCH!
OOPS! MY MISTAKE, WALTER. INSTEAD OF A STEAK SANDWICH, I SEEM TO HAVE GIVEN YOU A WOODEN STAKE SANDWICH! SILLY ME!
TOASTED SANDWICH
ALLOW US TO TOAST THAT SANDWICH FOR YOU, BUDDY!
SWEAT.
DRIP!
STEW!
GNEE-HEE! ALL THE SUN LAMPS WE COULD FIND!
SANDWICH – OR SAND WEDGE
OO-ER! WE'RE OFF TO SANDWICH TILL DAD COOLS DOWN. IT'S A TOWN IN KENT, HOPE IT'S FAR ENOUGH AWAY!
READ THE BEANO
OR THE EDITOR WILL BE FORCED TO THUMP YOU!
DIRECT BUS TO SANDWICH, KENT
GRR! WHERE ARE THOSE MENACES? TIME I LET THEM HAVE A TASTE OF MY SAND WEDGE! FUME!

OUT OF THEIR TREES!
WE HAVEN'T BEEN IN OUR TREE HOUSE FOR A WHILE!

GNUH? MY GNOSE SMELLS...
...SQUIRREL SQUATTERS!
HIYA!
HMM! LOOKS LIKE A NICE BIG NUT!
GNOUWCH!!!
CHOMP!
GNEOWL!
WAY-HEY-HEY!
YA-BOO!
C'MERE, YOU FOUR FURRY FACE-BITERS!
SUCKS!
GNASTY GNOSE GNIBBLERS!
MOTHER SQUIRREL.
THIS TREE HOUSE COULD DO WITH A DUST!
HUMPH! THAT'S SOFTY WORK!
WHISK! - DUST!
NOT WITH A TAIL LIKE MINE!
COUGH!
HACK!
COUGH! WE NEED A DRINK!
PHOOT!
WAH! NUTS!
GNUH? WHO'S NUTS?
THEIRS OF COURSE! THAT DOES IT!
HEE-HEE! WE SEE YOU FOUND OUR HOARD OF NUTS!
CHUCKLE!

SO –
THIS'LL GET THOSE HAIRY HORRORS OUT OF OUR TREE HOUSE.
GNEE-HEE!
SHOVE!
GNASH!
RIGHT, GNASHER! I'LL TURN THE TAP ON!
HOWEVER –
SILLY MENACES! THEY CAN'T OUTWIT US SHARP SQUIRRELS!
WAIT FOR IT, READERS!
PSST! WATCH THIS, READERS!
IN IT GOES.
WAIT A MINUTE! MY FOOT FEELS FUNNY.
WAARGH!!! WHAT'S THIS?
SUDDENLY –
OOFYAH!
GNULP!
WE THOUGHT IT WAS SQUIRRELS WHO HIBERNATED, NOT MENACES! HEE-HEE!
GNASH! WE'LL SORT THEM OUT, READER AFTER THE NEXT STORY. WAIT AND SE

MUM & DAD AT... BREAKING POINT!
WAAAAH! WE CAN'T STAND IT! SOB! WE'RE ONLY TWO THIRDS OF THE WAY THROUGH THIS ANNUAL AND DENNIS HAS BEEN MENACING ON EVERY PAGE!
EVERYONE HAS BEEN MOANING AND COMPLAINING TO US ABOUT HIM. AND GNASHER! AND BEA! RASHER, TOO! WAIL! SENDING US BILLS FOR THE DAMAGE. WAIL!
HEH-HEH!
YOU TWO NEED A BREAK! A NICE, RELAXING HOLIDAY! LET ME FIX IT UP FOR YOU, MUM AND DAD!
SOUNDS LOVELY, DENNIS!
SOUNDS SUPER!
HOTEL DE POSH? YES, WE'RE COMING TO VISIT! THAT'S MUM, DAD AND A COUPLE OF REALLY NICE MENACES. THAT'S ME AND GNASHER. WE'D LIKE A NICE ROOM, PLEASE! SEE YOU SHORTLY.
HOTEL DE POSH? FOR FOUR OF US? SOUNDS...EXPENSIVE!
SOUNDS ....TERRIBLE! THE MENACES ARE COMING! THE MENACES ARE COMING!!!
STAFF
HOTEL de POSH PRICES
1 NIGHT £££
2 NIGHTS £££
CONTINUED OVERLEAF

EEEK! THE MENACES ARE COMING!
LET US OUT OF HERE!
EVACUATE THE HOTEL!

HOTEL de POSH
FORMERLY HOTEL de BECKS
IF YOU HAVE TO ASK THE PRICE, YOU CAN'T AFFORD TO STAY HERE!
SCRAM!
THIS IS NOT A DRILL!
EVERY CHEF FOR HIMSELF!
RUN! RUN FOR YOUR LIVES!
WOMEN AND CHILDREN LAST - WAITERS FIRST!
NIGEL PARKINSON

The Menace family arrive—
STRANGE! THE HOTEL IS DESERTED! I THOUGHT IT WOULD BE BUSY!
I THOUGHT IT WOULD BE EXPENSIVE!
AND I THOUGHT THERE WOULD BE SOME STAFF. WAITERS AND THAT!
I STILL THOUGHT IT WOULD BE EXPENSIVE!
WELL, IT WOULD BE EXPENSIVE....
A weeks free holiday later —
...IF ALL THE STAFF WEREN'T TOO SCARED TO COME OUT AND GIVE US THE BILL! HEE-HEE! SOFTIES, ALL OF 'EM! HAW-HAW!
PHEW! THEY'RE LEAVING AT LAST!
GOOD RIDDANCE!
GNEE-HEE! JUST WHAT WE WANTED!
WELL, THAT WAS A LOVELY CHEAP HOLIDAY! WE'RE EVER SO RELAXED NOW.
YES, YOU TWO CAN GET ON WITH YOUR MENACING FOR THE REST OF THE ANNUAL NOW, WE DON'T CARE!

STILL OUT OF THEIR TREES!
OH-OH! THE MENACE IS ANGRY WITH US - JUST 'COS WE KNOCKED HIM OUT A FEW PAGES AGO!
AND TOOK OVER HIS TREE HOUSE!
GRR! YOU SQUIRREL SQUATTERS ARE DRIVING ME NUTS!

CHOMP!
CHOMP!
NO! DON'T NIBBLE THE LADDER!
WAAAH!
HAPPY LANDINGS!
OOF!
GNOOF!
AND –
PULL!
PYOING!
FIRE!
GOTCHA!
SPLOT!
YEUCH!
TITTER! NOW ISN'T THAT NICE! THE MENACES ARE BEING OUT-MENACED FOR A CHANGE!
GRRR!
GNASH!
SO –
LUCKILY, THOSE SQUIRRELS DON'T KNOW ABOUT OUR SECRET TUNNEL!
DIVE!
LET'S GO GET THEM!
IT GOES UP INSIDE THE TREE TRUNK. QUIETLY DOES IT.
AND –
SO! THINK YOU'RE STILL KEEPING US OUT, THEN?

YES! WE ARE, DENNIS! HEE-HEE!
NOD! NOD!
GOT YOU!
EH? WHAT? HOW DID YOU GET IN HERE?
YOU'RE JUST NO-GOOD SNEAKY, ROTTEN, MANGY VERMIN....
...WHICH IS WHY WE LIKE YOU! AND WHY WE'RE GOING TO FIND YOU A NEW PLACE TO LIVE!
THE SQUIRRELS LOVE THEIR NEW PAD!
DICKY BIRD BOX
OH, FURRY RUFFIANS!
TA, DENNIS! THIS IS A GREAT HOME!
BUT WALTER'S LOVE-BIRDS AREN'T TOO HAPPY ABOUT SHARING THEIR BIRD BOX WITH THEM! HAR-HAR!
WOW!
BIRDY BATH
NUTS! SLURP!

THE SOFTY WORLD OF SPORT
YOU KNOW, READERS, YOU DON'T HAVE TO BE A TOUGH MENACE TO DO THESE SPORTS. YOU CAN BE SOFT!
THESE GUYS ARE JUST HAVING A MUD PACK, LIKE ME! ONE MUST LOOK AFTER ONE'S SKIN, DON'T YOU KNOW!
HOW SIMPLY SOOPER! WALTER CAN LIFT TWO FRESHLY BAKED MERINGUES!
NNNNNNGHHHH!!!!!!
HOW STRONG, OUR PRINCE OF SOFTIES IS!

THOSE BOXERS WEAR GLOVES, TOO! GO SO WELL WITH MY NEW SLEEVELESS JUMPER! GLOVELY!
AND THESE CHAPS HAVE SET A NEW FASHION – SHOULDER PADS. IT'S WHAT ALL US HIP CATS ARE WEARING THIS SEASON.
ONE KNOWS HOW THE MOUNTAINEER FEELS. I NEED A MOUNTAIN OF ICING SUGAR FOR ALL THESE FAIRY CAKES I'VE BAKED!
BAKED BEAUTIFULLY, ONE MIGHT ADD.
I'VE GOT JIM-JAMS JUST LIKE THAT KARATE PERSON. JUST AS WELL, BECAUSE I'VE HAD A SOFT DAY'S SPORT. 'NIGHTY-'NIGHT, READERS!

Pram-tastic!
YOUR PRAM MAKES A SUPER SLEDGE, BEA!

YIPPEE! WE'RE THE FASTEST!
SWOOOSH!
GLOOP!
NO WAY, DENNIS! WE ARE!
TO PROVE IT, WE'LL HAVE A RACE!
YOU'RE ON!
RAZZ!
START FROM THE TOP!
WE'LL START WITH A BIT OF MENACING FROM BEA.
SO –
READY, MENACES?
NOT QUITE.
JUST GOT TO COLLECT MY LUCKY SNOWMAN.
GNEH?
THE RACE IS ON –
WHAT? WE'RE NOT MOVING!
HA-HA! BEA PUT ON HER CLOTHES INSIDE OUT SO SHE LOOKED LIKE A SNOWMAN!
WHY CAN'T WE MOVE?????
PSST! WE KNOW, DON'T WE, BEA?
YEAH, BIG BRUVVER!
WHEN BEA WAS LOOKING LIKE A SNOWMAN, SHE PUT A WHITE BLANKET ON THE SNOW IN FRONT OF THEM.
BAH! WE STILL CAN'T START!
YEEEHA! WE'VE WON!

YOU WON, BUT WE'RE NOT HAPPY ABOUT IT!
GREAT! A SNOWBALL FIGHT!
HAVE IT!
RASP!
TAKE COVER!
SOON –
BEA'S PRAM WAS A PERFECT SHIELD TO HIDE BEHIND!
ULP! WE'RE OUT OF SNOWBALLS!
WE'RE NOT!
GNATTACK!
SPLAT!
WHUP!
WHAP!
WAH!
ONE SNOWBALLING MASSACRE LATER –
TIME TO GO HOME. IN BEA'S PRAM, OF COURSE!
OH, NO! SOMEONE HAS CLOSED THE GARDEN GATE WHILE WE WERE GONE!
GNULP!
ZOOM!
CRASH!
LOOK AT THE STATE OF THE GATE! AND BEA'S PRAM!
WELL, I CAN FIX THEM, BUT I'LL NEED SOME PEACE AND QUIET WHILE I WORK.
SO WE'LL ALL POP OFF TO THE SUPERMARKET.
BUT AS YOU'VE RUINED HER PRAM, YOU'LL HAVE TO CARRY BEA, DENNIS!
OOO! STOP THAT, YOU LITTLE MENACE MONSTER!

'Twas the Night before Christmas,
When all through the house,
Not a creature was stirring...
Not even a Mouse...
CHEESE
RUBBISH! WE'RE STIRRING, ALL RIGHT!
YEAH! WE'RE OUTTA 'ERE! IT'S NOT SAFE! DENNIS IS GOING TO HAVE A - GULP! - CHRISTMAS PARTY!
TOO DANGEROUS FOR US MICE TO STAY!

THAT'S RIGHT, READERS! WE'RE GOING TO HAVE A CHRISTMAS PARTY! THESE ARE INVITES FOR ALL OUR PALS!
CURLY
HIYA, MENACES!
AHA! HERE'S OUR MATE, CURLY.
But –
OOOFPH!
THAT'S IT, CURLY! HAVE A GO ON OUR SLIDE!
CLANG!
SLI-I-I-I-DE!
GNOUCH!
PITY THE BIN STOPPED CURLY'S SLIDE! LOOKS LIKE IT'S STOPPED HIM COMING TO OUR PARTY! WE WON'T NEED HIS INVITE!
And –
I'M SURE OUR PAL, PIE-FACE, WON'T SAY NO TO A BIG CHRISTMAS FEED!
GNO WAY!
HUH? WHAT'S WRONG WITH PIE-FACE?
OO! MY POOR TUM! OOO! OOO! OO!
SILLY BOY! HE ATE ALL OUR MINCE PIES –60 IN ONE SITTING! HIS TUM HAS OVERLOADED!
HE'S JOINING CURLY IN HOSPITAL.
AS IT'S CHRISTMAS, WE'LL INVITE THE COLONEL AND SERGEANT SLIPPER.
I SAY, WHAT? PULL A CRACKER, OLD BEAN?
DELIGHTED!
DASH IT!
ELLO? WHAT'S ALL THIS, THEN?
WOW! ONE OF THE COLONEL'S HOME MADE CRACKERS!
BOOM!
So –
HUP! HUP! TAKE US TO THE FIELD HOSPITAL, MEN! QUICK, MARCH!
HUH! ANOTHER TWO NOT COMING TO OUR PARTY!
WHAT ABOUT OUR OLD BEANO PAL, LES PRETEND. WE'LL INVITE HIM.
GNUH? HE'S ALWAYS PRETENDING TO BE SOMETHING SILLY.
WOW! YOU'RE RIGHT, GNASHER! HE'S PRETENDING TO BE A SNOWMAN!
HE'S FROZEN STIFF! TAKE HIM TO HOSPITAL, THAWING OUT WARD!
FROZEN SOLID!

SHOVE!
WELL, LES CAN'T COME TO OUR PARTY, EITHER!
AMBULANCE
GNOT TO WORRY. HERE COMES 'ERBERT!
ARRGH!
LOOKS LIKE 'ERBERT IS JOINING LES IN HOSPITAL.
WELL, ALL OUR PALS CAN'T COME TO OUR PARTY, SO THERE'S ONLY ONE THING FOR IT. WE'LL INVITE THE SOFTIES!
GNEESH! YOU CANNOT BE SERIOUS!
He is!
WOULD YOU SOFT CHAPS BE SO KIND AS TO ACCEPT AN INVITATION TO OUR CHRISTMAS PARTY?
GASP! WE CAN'T BELIEVE OUR SOFT LITTLE EARS!
HOW VERY.....KIND!
MY PRECIOUS AND HIS CHUMS! THEY'VE FAINTED WITH SURPRISE!
FAINT!
COLLAPSE!
SWOON!
THEY'RE NOT USED TO DENNIS BEING NICE TO THEM!
DENNIS WAS...NICE!
THIS PATIENT IS HALLUCINATING!
NEENAW! NEENAW!
THE SOFTIES ARE OFF TO HOSPITAL, TO RECOVER FROM THE SHOCK!
Then –
BAH! EVERYONE IS SPENDING CHRISTMAS IN HOSPITAL. EXCEPT US!
FEEBLE PLOP!
GNOBODY AT OUR PARTY.
SO THERE'S ONLY ONE THING FOR IT, READERS!
GYEAH!
HAPPY CHRISTMAS
TO
EVERYONE
COLONEL TO NURSE...BEDPAN REQUIRED! OVER!
WE'LL HAVE OUR PARTY HERE! WAHEY! HAPPY CHRISTMAS, EVERYONE!
BLOW!
NO

FINALLY — THE LAST RUDE WORD YOU CAN GET AWAY WITH!
PLONKER!
HOW DARE YOU CALL ME THAT, ILL-SPOKEN CHILD!
WRONG, WALTER! A PLONKER ISSA LARGE MARBLE! LOOK IT UP IN DA DIKSHUNERY!
SHE'S RIGHT AGAIN! NOW WHY DON'T YOU GO AND LOOK UP A DICTIONARY TO FIND MORE RUDE WORDS YOU CAN GET AWAY WITH, READERS?

EXTRA! EXTRA!
READ ALL ABOUT IT!
SHOCK NEWS - SOFTY IN SHOCK SHOCK!
B-B-B-BE QUIET, DENNIS! NOTHING HAS SHOCKED THIS SOFTY!
BEANO
SOFTY IN SHOCK SHOCK!
GNOT YET, MAYBE. BUT WAIT TILL I BURST THIS! WALTER WILL BURST INTO TEARS! GNEE-HEE!
STOP PRESS
FOR MORE SHOCKS, SURPRISES, LAUGHS AND MENACING -
BUY THE BEANO ON SALE EVERY THURSDAY

WALTER THE SOFTY
Sponsored by Puffo Cosmetics
SOFTIES WOULDN'T GIVE A PUFF FOR ANYTHING ELSE!

RASHER
Sponsored by Beanotown Cleansing Department
AND ALL BECAUSE THE PIG WILL EAT ANYTHING!
OINKY -YUM!
DISGUSTING!
VILE!
THE SHAME!